Adventure Story Bible
Book 10

King David's
Reign

Written by Anne de Graaf

Illustrated by José Pérez Montero

Bible Society

King David's Reign

Contents — 2 Samuel 11—24; Psalms 32, 51, 3, 63, 18; 1 Kings 2;
1 Chronicles 11, 21—22; 2 Chronicles 3

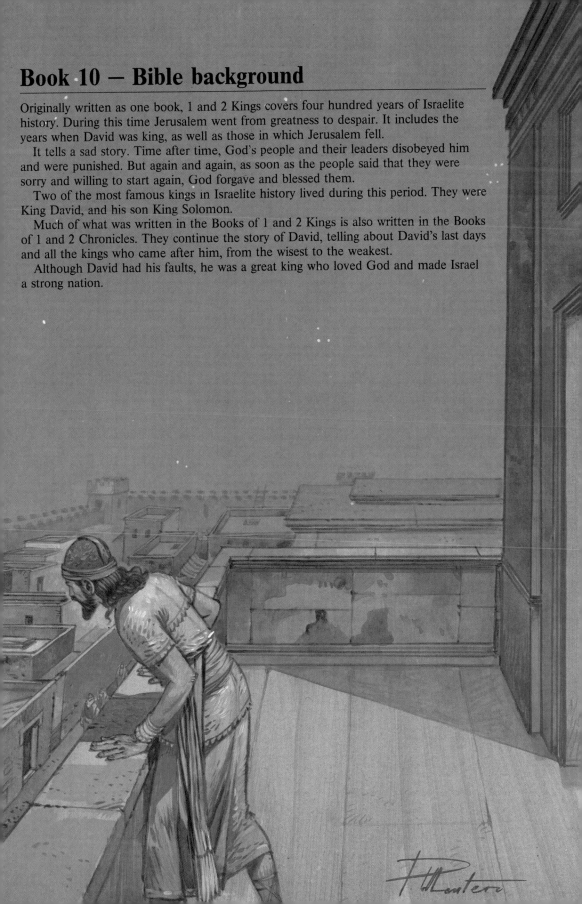

Book 10 — Bible background

Originally written as one book, 1 and 2 Kings covers four hundred years of Israelite history. During this time Jerusalem went from greatness to despair. It includes the years when David was king, as well as those in which Jerusalem fell.

It tells a sad story. Time after time, God's people and their leaders disobeyed him and were punished. But again and again, as soon as the people said that they were sorry and willing to start again, God forgave and blessed them.

Two of the most famous kings in Israelite history lived during this period. They were King David, and his son King Solomon.

Much of what was written in the Books of 1 and 2 Kings is also written in the Books of 1 and 2 Chronicles. They continue the story of David, telling about David's last days and all the kings who came after him, from the wisest to the weakest.

Although David had his faults, he was a great king who loved God and made Israel a strong nation.

DAVID'S WEAKNESSES

His own worst enemy

2 Samuel 11.1–2

King David was a very great king. His armies won more battles than anyone else's. But this was not the reason David was so great. King David loved God very much. Ever since the prophet Samuel had anointed David, and God's spirit came upon David, he had known God was with him in a very special way. There was one thing David wanted more than anything else, and that was to please God. This made him great.

David didn't want his own way all the time. Instead, he let God lead his life. He sang about God being his shepherd, and asked God to be the shepherd of his life. David wanted to please God, and God loved and blessed him.

David had to fight many wars while he was king. Thanks to God's help, he won most of them. The one battle he did lose, however, was very important. It was a battle where David became his own worst enemy, because he did something he knew God would not like.

It happened one spring, after David had sent his armies to fight the Ammonites. David was working in his palace. He had an afternoon nap, then climbed the stairs to the palace roof. He paced back and forth, letting the cool air refresh his mind. As he walked, he listened to the sounds of the city below him. There were babies crying, men laughing, and the clatter of pots as evening meals were prepared.

David stopped to listen. Then he heard a woman's voice, quite close by, singing softly. David looked down into the courtyard below him. The choices David would make because of what he saw then would be the reasons why he became his own worst enemy.

David is tempted

2 Samuel 11.3–4

David looked down from the palace roof into a courtyard quite close by.

He saw a woman standing by a tub of water, having her bath. David was overcome with her beauty. He could not move, but waited for her to finish bathing. When she stood up again to dry herself, David thought, "I have never seen such a beautiful woman." She quickly put her robe on, then went into her house.

As David watched her go, he felt he must find out who she was. He went back into the palace, and ordered a servant to find out her name.

When the man returned he said, "The woman is Bathsheba, the wife of Uriah the Hittite." Uriah the Hittite was one of David's special guard, one of his most trusted fighting men.

David thought for a moment. Uriah was away, fighting the Ammonites. He struggled between what he wanted very much and what he knew God would want him to do. He did not ask God's help in deciding what to do. Instead, David made his own choice. He sent messengers to get Bathsheba and bring her to the palace.

4

When they brought her in, David motioned for the servants to leave. He could do nothing but look at Bathsheba, he found her so beautiful.

David does what he wants

2 Samuel 11.5-13

David slept with Bathsheba, just as if they were married to each other. David had many wives already, as often happened in those days. Bathsheba was already married to Uriah the Hittite. Because of this, it was very wrong of David to act as if Bathsheba was his wife. David broke God's law when he chose Bathsheba rather than wanting to please God.

David sent Bathsheba back to her home. In the weeks that followed, David tried not to think about what had happened. In less than two months he received a message from Bathsheba. She was going to have a baby and David was the father. Now everyone would know what David had done!

David acted quickly. There was only one way he could hide the fact that he had slept with another man's wife. If he could get Uriah the Hittite to sleep with Bathsheba as soon as possible, then no one would know the baby was David's. When the baby was born, everyone would think it was Uriah's and his secret would be safe.

David sent word to General Joab. "Send Uriah the Hittite to Jerusalem," he said. When Uriah arrived David asked him how the battle was going. Then he told him to take the day off, go home, and relax. He even sent Uriah a gift. But Uriah was a good soldier. In fact, he was one of David's best soldiers. So instead of going home, he slept near the palace. He didn't want to be off duty while the rest of David's men were out at battle.

The next morning David sent for Uriah again. "Why didn't you go home last night?" he asked.

"How could I do such a thing?" Uriah asked. "All my friends and the generals are sleeping in the open fields in tents, and the Lord's Covenant Box is with them." The Lord's Covenant Box contained the commandments God had given to Moses. "How could I go home and relax with my wife when so many of Israel's men are out fighting and not able to enjoy themselves? I would never do such a thing!"

So David invited Uriah to eat dinner with him that evening, and gave Uriah so much to drink that he got drunk. But even then he didn't go home.

David becomes a murderer

2 Samuel 11.14–26

David felt desperate. All he wanted to do was cover up his wrong action. But it was proving harder than he had thought. One wrong led to another.

When David couldn't get Uriah to go home, he came up with another plan. The next morning David sent for Uriah again. He ordered him to return to the battlefield, and he gave him a letter for General Joab.

Uriah didn't know, but in the letter David had ordered his death! He had told Joab to put Uriah wherever the fighting was at its worst, so that Uriah would be killed by the enemy.

When Uriah reached the battleground he gave the letter to Joab. Joab followed David's orders, and before the next battle was over the Ammonites had killed Uriah.

Joab sent a messenger to David with the full story. "General Joab ordered his troops to surround the city of Rabbah. But when they were close to the city walls, the enemy shot arrows at them. Some of the king's men died and Uriah the Hittite was one of them."

When David heard that his plan had worked, he breathed a sigh of relief. "Tell Joab not to be upset," David said, "as you can never tell who will die in battle. Press on and destroy the city."

When news of Uriah's death reached Bathsheba, she cried for many days, and mourned for him.

The broken king

2 Samuel 11.27—12.15

Some time after Uriah's death David sent
word to Bathsheba that he wanted her to
become his wife. Bathsheba went to the palace
and married David. A few months later their
baby boy was born.

God was not happy — he knew David had
been wicked. David could not hide from God
that he had taken another man's wife, then
killed her husband.

So the Lord sent his prophet Nathan to see
David. Nathan told David a story. "There were
two men," Nathan said. "One was rich and the
other poor. The rich man had many sheep
and cattle, but the poor man had only one
little lamb. He took care of it and soon the
tiny lamb was like a child to him, sharing his
food and drinking from his cup. The lamb
even slept in his arms.

"But then a traveller came to visit the rich
man. Instead of killing one of his own sheep
and eating it, the rich man killed the poor
man's lamb and served it for dinner."

"Who could do such a terrible thing!" David
exploded. "That rich man deserves to die! He
must pay for that lamb four times over!"

But Nathan turned to the king and said,
"You are that man! This is what the Lord
says, 'I gave you many wives, and a great
kingdom, as well. If this had not been enough
I would have given you even more. So why
did you choose to kill Uriah the Hittite?'

"The Lord says, 'Because you have done
this thing, your sons will fight each other. You
will not die, but because you have not taken
the Lord seriously, your baby will die.' "

David hung his head. The Lord's words
pierced his heart like a sword. He knew God
was right. The wrong he had done could
never be kept secret from God. David said,
"I have sinned against the Lord."

David is forgiven

2 Samuel 12.15–25; Psalms 32, 51

David did not try and make excuses for what he had done. He didn't try to hide or cover up his wrong, but bravely admitted that it was a terrible thing to do. He knew it was very wrong. "Please give me a clean heart, God," David prayed.

The Lord heard David and forgave him. David had not tried to put the blame on anyone else. The Lord let him start again. One of the psalms of David is about how God forgives, and doesn't stop loving his people. David wrote, "The Lord never stops loving the man who trusts in him."

David knew the Lord would love him for ever, but he also knew he could not undo the wrong his choices had caused. After Nathan left David, the little boy who had been born to David and Bathsheba became very sick.

David begged God to make the baby better. David refused to eat any food, and lay on the ground all night and prayed.

After seven days the baby died. David's servants were afraid to tell him the news. But when he heard them whispering he asked, "Is the child dead?"

"Yes," they replied, "he's dead."

Then David got up, took a bath, put on new clothes and went to the house of the Lord. There he prayed to God and thanked him again for forgiving him.

When David returned to the palace he sat down and ate a hearty meal. His servants whispered to each other, "The king cried while the baby lived, but now that he's dead, he eats as if nothing has happened."

David said, "While the child lived, there was still a chance the Lord might save him. But now there is no reason not to eat. Will that bring the child back? No, when I die, I will go to where the boy is, but he will never come back to me."

Then David went to Bathsheba. First she had lost her husband, now she had lost her

baby. She felt deeply unhappy. David loved Bathsheba, and wanted her to stop feeling sad. He comforted her, and they promised to take care of each other.

After this Bathsheba became pregnant, and she and David had another child. It was a boy and they named him Solomon, which meant "Peaceful."

The Lord chose Solomon to be very special. He sent word through Nathan the prophet that the baby should also be called Jedidiah, which meant "Loved by the Lord."

A family feud

2 Samuel 13.1–39

As the years went by, David's many children grew older. The Lord had warned David that he would be punished for killing Uriah. One of the punishments was that David's children would quarrel. This began to happen as the children grew up. One of the worst arguments took place between the two half-brothers, Amnon and Absalom.

Amnon fell in love with his half-sister,

Tamar. Amnon could think of nothing else but Tamar and how beautiful she was. He dreamt so much about her, he couldn't eat. One of Amnon's friends came up with a plan.

Amnon pretended to be ill and sent for Tamar to come and take care of him. But when he sent the servants out of the room, he seized her and said, "Come to bed with me."

"No!" she said to him. "Don't force me. Don't do this wicked thing. What about me? How could I ever live with the shame? And what about you? You would be disgraced!"

But Amnon refused to listen to her.

Because he was stronger than Tamar, he forced her to do what he wanted. But then he hated her even more than he had loved her. "Get up and get out!" he shouted.

Tamar ran to her brother Absalom's house, weeping. Absalom took her in and said he would take care of her. When David heard about Amnon hurting Tamar, he was furious. Absalom hated his brother so much for what he had done to Tamar that he wouldn't even speak to him.

Two years later Absalom set a trap for Amnon, to revenge him for what he had done to Tamar. He invited all the princes to a sheep-shearing party. Then he waited until Amnon was drunk, and ordered his men to kill him.

When the rest of David's sons saw what had happened, they jumped on their mules and rode as fast as they could back to Jerusalem. They were all so sad! For many days afterwards David cried about his dead son.

Absalom knew his father would be very angry with him for having killed Amnon, so he ran away to a little country called Geshur, and lived there for three years.

DAVID'S SON ABSALOM
Forgiving Absalom

2 Samuel 14.1-33

David mourned the death of his son Amnon. But after some time he realized he had lost more than one son. When Absalom left the country, David had lost another son, too. When a few years had passed, David wished that Absalom could come home. He loved his son and missed him. Yet he knew that Absalom had done something very wrong.

General Joab watched King David considering whether or not he should ask Absalom to come home. Joab knew that, on the one hand, David loved his son, but on the other, it was hard to ignore what Absalom had done in killing his brother. Joab came up with a plan which would bring Absalom home.

Joab asked a wise woman to go to David and tell him a story. She was to pretend the story was true. The woman dressed in mourning clothes and wore no make-up, as if she had been mourning for a long time. She pretended to be very sad. She told him she had lost one son because his brother had killed him. Then she asked David if she should ask her second son to come home, because unless she was protected by the king's word, someone might kill the second son also, in revenge. He was the only family she had left.

David took a good look at the wise woman and said, "I will make sure your other son is not harmed." After David had said that, she mentioned the banishment of the king's own son, Absalom. This story of the wise woman

13

was like the story of Absalom and Amnon. The king had judged that it would be good for the widow's banished son to come home, and it pointed out to David what he could do about Absalom.

Then David asked her, "Did Joab put you up to this?" She nodded and praised David's own wisdom in knowing what she was really saying by her story.

It was David's heart's desire to bring his own son back to Jerusalem. David went and found Joab, and smiled at his friend. "Go on," he said, "bring Absalom home."

Joab was glad. David and Absalom belonged together. But when Absalom was back in Jerusalem, David refused to see him.

Two years went by until Absalom wanted to see his father so much that he sent for Joab. Twice Joab refused to come to him, so Absalom set fire to one of Joab's fields. That brought Joab running!

"Why did you set fire to my field?" he demanded.

"Because you wouldn't see me, and I wanted to see the king!" Absalom said. "If I've done such a bad thing, then let the king punish me. I've waited such a long time. What was the point of bringing me to Jerusalem if I'm not allowed to see my father?"

Joab went and talked to the king. Then David sent for Absalom and welcomed him with a kiss. Father and son were together again.

Absalom tries to become king

2 Samuel 15.1–12

Absalom knew he was next in line to the throne after David died, but he wanted to become king right away.

So after Absalom had been reunited with David he did something bad. He plotted about how he could become king instead of David. Absalom was clever and cunning. He spent time trying to make himself more popular than David.

Every day Absalom went to the city gates. He drove his chariot and horses and had fifty men running ahead of him, so that anyone entering the city could see Absalom was important and powerful.

At the gates he talked to all the people who had brought their complaints to the king and told them that there was no representative of King David to hear their case. "Yet the law is on your side," Absalom would say. "If only I were a judge, then I could give you justice."

The people nodded. "Yes," they said, "Absalom would make a good judge."

By doing these things Absalom managed to win the hearts of the people of Israel.

After four years in Jerusalem, Absalom was ready to spring his trap. He went to his father and asked if he could go to Hebron, which is where Saul lived when he was king. Many of David's best fighting men went with Absalom, as well as Ahithophel, one of David's best advisers. They went in good faith, not knowing what Absalom was about to do.

Slowly, but surely, Absalom collected men until he had a great force. Absalom had become more popular with the people than David, and they wanted Absalom to be king instead of him.

15

David on the run again

2 Samuel 15.13–23; Psalms 3, 63

When a messenger came and told David, "Many men of Israel want Absalom to be king, rather than you!" David knew he was in trouble.

"This is very serious," David thought to himself. "I know Absalom. He'll kill us all, if that's what it takes for him to become king." David was not ready to fight. He had no choice but to run away from Jerusalem. "If I stay, Absalom will kill us all," he said to his men.

"We'll follow you whatever happens," they replied. So David led his wives and children, loyal soldiers, servants, and ministers out of Jerusalem. He left only ten women behind to take care of the palace.

While the crowd marched on, King David watched as line after line of men, together with their families, filed past. His support was great, but he knew he did not have as many followers as Absalom.

Among the crowd were six hundred soldiers who had followed him from Gath, a non-Israelite tribe. "Why should you leave Jerusalem?" David said to them. "Go back. There's no reason for you to wander with us. I don't even know where we're going yet! Go back and stay with the new king, and may the Lord be kind to you."

But Ittai their leader said, "It doesn't matter if we're marching to life or death. As sure as the Lord lives wherever the king goes, that's where we, your servants, will be. We will never leave your side!"

David looked down. These people were not

16

even Israelites yet they were faithful to him, but his own son had driven him away. "March on, then," he said.

The people watched and cried loudly as King David and his followers marched quickly out of Jerusalem.

David's followers headed towards the desert where they would be safe, at least for a little while, from Absalom and his army.

That night as David slept under the stars he remembered the long years he had spent running away from King Saul. He wrote a song about his feelings. "Lord, no matter what people may say, I know you will protect me from all those who want to hurt me. I will not worry, however many they are. I will sleep and be peaceful because you will rescue me. Lord, above all, please bring peace to your people." David trusted God to be with him. "Oh God," he said, "your love is better than life! As I lie in bed I think about you; I think about what you have done for me in the past. Because you are my help, I come close to you and feel safe."

Spies

2 Samuel 15.24-37

The next morning David went to find Zadok, the priest who had come with him bringing the Lord's Covenant Box. The Covenant Box contained the commandments that God had given Moses. He said to him, "Take the Covenant Box back into the city. If God is pleased with me, he will bring me back and let me see it. But if he says I should not be king any more, then he's right. Let him do to me whatever seems good to him."

As Zadok and the Levite priests were getting ready to go, David said, "When you and the other priest Abiathar go back, take your two sons with you. If you hear anything you think I should know, send your sons to me. I will wait in the desert for them."

The priests nodded. It was a dangerous mission, but they would do anything, even risk their sons, in order to help the king whom God had chosen, the great King David.

David was so sad about leaving everything behind that he cried as he marched on, leading his people away from Jerusalem. When he reached a hill called the Mount of Olives, he went up it bare-footed, and with his head covered. When he reached the top, an old friend called Hushai met him there.

David said to him, "I need your help, but there's nothing you can do if you come with me. Why not be my spy instead, and return to Jerusalem? Offer to serve Absalom with good advice, but give him bad advice instead. Every time he gets good advice from Ahithophel, who was my best adviser but is now a traitor, say something different. That way Absalom will not be successful. My priests, Zadok and Abiathar, will be there, too. Tell them what you hear and their sons will pass it on to me."

Hushai nodded. He hurried all the way back to Jerusalem and arrived just as Absalom entered the city.

The two advisers

2 Samuel 16.15–17.29

David's friend Hushai pushed his way through the crowd which surrounded Absalom, the new king. He bowed down before Absalom and cried out, "Long live the king! Long live the king!"

Absalom turned to him and said, "What do you mean, Hushai? Why didn't you follow your friend, my father?"

Hushai said, "But the Lord has chosen you. I will serve you, just as I served your father."

Absalom thought to himself, "Yes, so many others have come over to my side. Why not this wise man Hushai?"

Hushai looked at Ahithophel, Absalom's adviser. Ahithophel had been King David's best adviser. He was always right. Yet Ahithophel had betrayed David and followed his son, Absalom. David had called

Ahithophel a traitor and wanted his friend Hushai to disagree with him at every opportunity.

Soon Ahithophel said, "Take twelve thousand men and hunt David down tonight. Hurry, while he is still discouraged and tired from running away. When you catch David, make sure he's the only one you kill. Then all the people will call you their leader. Once David is dead, even his closest friends and family will become your followers."

Ahithophel's advice had never been wrong yet. If Absalom had followed Ahithophel's

advice, he would most probably have won. But David hoped Absalom would ask Hushai for his advice, and Absalom did!

"Where is Hushai? I want to hear what he has to say, too," Absalom said.

When Hushai heard what Ahithophel had said he told Absalom, "Oh no! That was very bad advice! It would be much better to leave David alone for a while. David is such a great fighter, he is probably already hiding in the caves, just as he used to do when Saul chased him. Wait until you can get all your troops together, from the whole of Israel, north to south, then lead them in battle against David. Wait until you have every man at your side."

Absalom liked the idea of being the leader of a big army and thought this plan would be more successful, so he took Hushai's advice. But Ahithophel knew Absalom's choice would lead only to his death and the return of David to Jerusalem. Ahithophel did not want to be caught by King David as a traitor. He had made a big mistake. He had chosen to follow Absalom rather than David, God's choice as king. Ahithophel went home and hanged himself.

Late that same night, Hushai got word to the two priests' sons. "Run and tell David to hurry across the River Jordan. I've bought him a little time, but he must hurry. Run quickly now and tell him!"

The two sons disappeared into the night. But a young man saw them and told Absalom, who sent out men to find them.

The priests' sons had run quickly and had been hidden in a well. When Absalom's men arrived, they couldn't find the boys, so they returned to Absalom empty-handed. Then the priests' sons hurried to King David's camp and gave him the news.

All that night David and his people crossed the river, until by morning there was no one left on the shore. David breathed a sigh of relief. Now his men had at least a fighting chance.

A tree catches Absalom

2 Samuel 18.1-33

The next morning David quickly divided his men into groups. While Absalom was waiting for all his troops to arrive in Jerusalem, David's position became stronger and stronger. He chose a forest as the place for the battle and waited for Absalom's army to catch up with him.

David's troops got ready for the battle, and David wanted to join them. But his generals said, "No! You are worth ten thousand of us. You must stay here, safe from harm."

So David did as they said and stayed behind. As the troops walked past him David ordered them, "If you catch Absalom, don't hurt him. Even if he is trying to take away my throne, he's still my son!"

When David's troops met Absalom's army there was a terrible battle. Men fought all over the countryside and many died in the forest.

At one point Absalom, who was riding with his men, got caught in a tree. Absalom's long, thick hair tangled in the branches, but his donkey kept on going. One of David's men saw this and hurried back to General Joab. "I've seen Absalom and he's helpless, hanging from a tree by his hair!"

"You fool!" Joab shouted. "Why didn't you finish him off? You could have earned a bonus for yourself. Don't you know he's the enemy?"

"But he's the king's son!" the soldier said. "And you heard the king order us not to harm Absalom!"

Joab would not listen. "I'm not wasting time with you," he said. He ran up to Absalom and killed him while he was hanging from the tree. Then he threw the body into a pit and covered it with stones. Joab sounded the trumpet and the troops stopped fighting. David's men had won!

When news reached David that the battle was over, he was not excited. All he could ask was, "What about Absalom? Tell me, is young Absalom safe?"

The messenger shook his head and said, "He's far from safe. I wish all your enemies could end up like him!"

Then David knew his son was dead. Instead of being happy that his army had won, David was very upset and cried bitterly because Absalom had died. "Oh my son Absalom! If only I had died instead of you!" he cried. "Absalom, Absalom! My son, my son!"

David returns to Jerusalem

2 Samuel 19.1–39

"The king is crying for Absalom," David's soldiers told each other. Instead of singing songs and feeling proud of the way they had fought for their king, David's men didn't know what to think.

"Wasn't Absalom the enemy?" they whispered to each other.

When General Joab heard that the king was crying and mourning Absalom's death, he was angry. He marched over to David and roared, "What do you think you're doing? Your men risked their lives for you today! Do you want them to think you were on Absalom's side rather than on their side? Go out there and tell your men you are proud of them. If you don't, I swear that by morning you won't have any army left."

David overcame his feelings and nodded. He knew Joab was right. David sat where the men could see him, thanking and praising them for the great battle they had fought that day for him.

Once news of his victory had spread David heard that the Israelites wanted him to go back to Jerusalem and be king. So King David

sent a message to the leaders of Judah saying, "Why haven't you come and told me I'm welcome in Jerusalem now that Absalom is dead? Why let the rest of Israel ask for me to come back, while you don't? You are my relatives, after all." David also told them that their general, Amasa, could be in charge of the army instead of Joab.

When the men of Judah heard David's message it won their loyalty, and they remembered how they had loved and followed David in the past. "Yes!" they cried out. "Come back and be our king!"

So David and his wives, children, servants, and soldiers all trekked back to the River Jordan. Then the men of Judah welcomed David and all his people, and escorted them across the water.

Some of the people who came to meet David were those who had betrayed him to follow Absalom. They came to David with their excuses, and he forgave them all.

THE REIGN OF DAVID

One general against another

2 Samuel 19.40–20.11

When the men of Israel who had first wanted David to return as king saw the men of Judah escort David and his family across the River Jordan, they were jealous. "What gives them the right to be David's favourites?" they asked. Then an argument started between the people of Israel and the people of Judah about who was closest to David as king. The tribes of Israel and Judah became angry with one another, even though they both belonged to the same nation now.

There was a troublemaker called Sheba who belonged to one of the Israelite tribes. He said, "Down with David! Don't follow him! We don't want him, anyway!" So the men of Israel deserted David and followed Sheba, but the men of Judah remained loyal to their king and followed him all the way from the Jordan to Jerusalem.

When David reached Jerusalem he ordered his new general, Amasa, to spend the next three days gathering all the troops together so they could run after Sheba and catch him.

"Report to me at the palace in three days," David said. But Amasa took longer than three days. So David told one of his other generals to take all the men and start chasing Sheba. "Amasa has taken too long," he said, "and Sheba will cause more trouble than Absalom ever did."

As the troops hunted down Sheba, they came across General Amasa on his way back to Jerusalem. Joab, who had been David's general before Amasa, thought to himself, "Here's my chance to pay him back."

Joab came forward to meet Amasa, and his sword happened to fall on the ground. Joab stepped towards Amasa. "How are you, my friend?" he said, and took hold of Amasa's beard to kiss him. Amasa wasn't on guard against the sword Joab was holding in his other hand, so Joab stabbed and killed Amasa.

When Amasa fell dead on the road, one of Joab's men called to the troops, "Whoever is for Joab and for David, follow Joab!"

The nation is united

2 Samuel 20.12–26; 1 Kings 2.5–6

David's soldiers were not sure what they should do when they saw how treacherously Joab had killed Amasa. One of Joab's men saw them stop and stare at the body, so he quickly moved the body into a field and covered it. Then the men followed General Joab, chasing after Sheba.

Soon the soldiers found the town where the traitor Sheba was hiding. They started to batter down the walls of the city, but a wise woman came out to talk to them. "Bring Joab here," she said. "I want to talk with him."

When Joab came to her she said, "What is it you want? Surely whatever it is, it's not worth destroying a town of people who follow the Lord God."

Joab told her that he didn't want to destroy the town, but he was looking for Sheba. The wise woman went back into the town and told the people that it was better to turn Sheba over to David's men than for the whole city to be destroyed. They cut off Sheba's head and threw it over the wall to Joab, so Joab sent all his soldiers back home.

But Joab would pay for the murder he had committed. Many years later, when David told his son Solomon how he should rule the kingdom, he ordered that Joab should be punished. Solomon saw that the order was carried out. Joab would pay for the murders he had committed, and the price would be his own life.

David's greatest men

2 Samuel 23.8–39; 1 Chronicles 11.10–47

In the years after David returned to Jerusalem his kingdom became a safe place to live in. This was because of God's protection and because David had such good fighting men in his army. These soldiers were famous throughout the land.

David and his men had fought side by side ever since the early days when King Saul chased David up one side of the country and down the other. Of these fighting men, there were three who were most famous of all, and another thirty-four who were very famous.

Through all that had happened, David's mighty men had stayed close beside him. They protected their king and made sure no one ever took David's crown away from him. They were David's bodyguard, and there was nothing they would not do for him.

During one battle David and his men fought the Philistines. The enemy was camped in Bethlehem, David's home town. David and his great men were sitting in a cave, working out a battle plan. Three of them overheard David sigh and say, "Oh, how I long for a drink of Bethlehem water from the well by the gate."

These three men crept away and very carefully made their way through the enemy lines. They went into the Philistine camp, drew some water from the well, and hurried back to the safety of their own camp.

When David saw the water they brought him, he was amazed. "I can't drink this!" he said. "It would be like drinking the blood of these men who risked their lives." So he poured the water out as an offering to the Lord.

This is just one story of how extremely brave the men of David were. There were many more stories about their bravery and cunning. With their help the Lord continued to look after David down through the years.

Thanks to God

2 Samuel 21.15–22.51; Psalm 18

David ruled as king over both Israel and Judah. There were no more enemies from inside the kingdom, but the Philistines attacked Israel over and over again.

Sometimes David went with his soldiers to fight them, but he was beginning to get tired of fighting. So David's men made him promise to stay in Jerusalem. "We'll make sure you never have to fight in a battle again. If you were to die, it would be like the lamp of Israel going out," they said.

But it did not matter whether or not David was with his army. The Lord blessed David and everything he did, including his armies. Israel won great battles against its enemies during those last years of David's reign as king.

As David grew older he knew more than ever that his success was given to him from the Lord. He wrote a beautiful song for God, a prayer of thanks for saving him from enemies like Saul and the Philistines.

"I owe everything to God," David said. "I call to the Lord, who is worthy of praise, and he saves me from my enemies. It is God who gives me strength. He shows me how to live, and shows love to the one he has chosen. He will do the same for my descendants, too." David trusted God for everything.

David knew he had not always done exactly what God wanted. He didn't pretend he was always right. He openly spoke of his wrong and said he was sorry. God was pleased with David for doing this, as it showed him that he had a good heart, even if he sometimes did wrong things. David asked God to forgive him, and he promised to love and honour the Lord even more than before.

David dreams of the future

2 Samuel 24.1–25; 1 Chronicles 21.1–22.1;
2 Chronicles 3.1

While David was king he wanted to find out exactly how many people there were in Israel.

Joab knew the Lord would not be happy about David trying to measure his greatness. He tried to talk David out of counting all his people, but David wouldn't listen. So Joab had to do what David wanted.

When Joab had finished counting he told David that there were 1,300,000 men who could fight in the army. But by then David knew he had made a mistake. "I've done a terrible thing," he said to the Lord. "Please forgive me," he prayed.

The next day the prophet Gad came to tell David that the Lord would punish him, and God sent a terrible sickness to the kingdom. David was very sad when he saw his people falling ill and dying.

"Why punish them?" he cried out.

Gad went to David and told him he should build an altar and say he was sorry to the Lord. The place where the altar should be built was a large, flat threshing floor, where grains of wheat were separated from the stalks.

David did what the prophet told him. He bought the land where the threshing floor was and worshipped God. Then the Lord answered David's prayers and the illness stopped spreading.

Because of this David said, "This is where the temple of the Lord God will be built. This altar will be the one at which the Israelites worship." No longer would the Covenant Box have to stay in a tent.

For years David had wanted to build a magnificent temple for God, but he knew he wasn't the one to build it. God wanted to give

that job to David's son, Solomon. Now David knew where that temple would stand.

In the centuries to come that place would be very holy, the site of God's temple in Jerusalem. It would be where God's people from far and wide would come to sacrifice to God, praying for help and thanking him for his blessings.

David's final words

2 Samuel 23.1-7; 1 Kings 2.1-4

God loved David very much, and David loved God. When David sinned against God he would come to God and say he was sorry. Not many kings would choose to do that.

In one of his last songs David wrote, "A king who rules with justice, doing what God wants and not lying or hiding anything, is like the sun shining in a cloudless sky, the sun that makes the grass sparkle after the rain."

David was not afraid of dying. He knew that God loved him, and that he had made a promise to bless David's descendants for ever. He thought about his son Solomon and all the troubles he would have to face after David had gone. He called Solomon to his bedside.

"My son," he said, "the time has come for me to die. Be confident and determined, and do what the Lord your God asks of you. Obey him and keep his laws. Do this, and you will have his blessing."

Solomon listened to his dying father, the king. He would be the new king, even though he was not next in line. Solomon had elder brothers, but he was David's choice and he was God's choice. The advice he heard was wise, and he listened to it, hoping for strength and more wisdom in the hard days ahead.

The advice David gave his son was a model for all future rulers of the people of Israel. Some would not listen to this advice and would turn away from God. But some would follow in David's footsteps, loving God and trying to obey him.

Adventure Story Bible   Old Testament

New Testament